MW00489642

Why You're My Bestie

You are the best

_____

in the world.

2

You have the best taste in

_____ .

3

You give the best advice about

_____ .

4

I still laugh about the time

_____

and

_____ .

5

I am completely jealous of your

_____ .

You can cheer me up just by

_____

7

You have the funniest

_____ .

You

_____

the best

_____

ever.

I'd be lost without your

_____ .

10

You are crazy-talented at

_____ .

11

You have the best

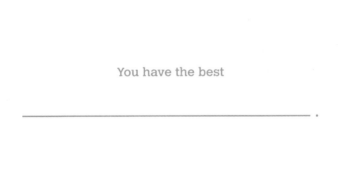

12

If you wanted to, you could easily

_____ .

13

I enjoy bragging to other people about your

_____ .

14

You deserve the Best

Award.

15

If you were a holiday, you'd be

_____ .

16

I have the best time going to

_____

with you.

17

_____

always reminds me of you.

18

We'd make the best

---

team.

19

It is fantastic how you

_____

when you

_____ .

Your

_____

should be studied by science.

21

You're the best at giving

_____ .

22

I love how you

———————————————————————

every day.

23

If you were an animal, you'd be

_____ .

24

You make me want to be a better

_____ .

25

I wish I knew your secret for

_____ .

26

It would be the best to see you

_____ .

27

I love watching people react when you

_____ .

28

Everyone should be as

_____

as you.

29

You make the best

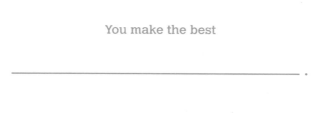

It's the best to play

.

with you.

31

I believe the world needs your unique

_____ .

32

_____

and

_____

should play us in the movie about our friendship.

33

You get my

_____

better than anyone.

We should totally

_____

someday.

35

You just keep getting better at

_____ .

36

You deserve the best

_____

37

If we could bottle your

_____

and sell it, we'd make a fortune.

38

It is supremely funny when you

_____ .

39

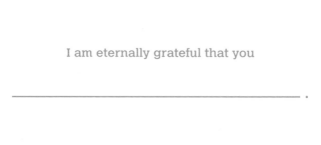

I am eternally grateful that you

———————————————————————————— .

40

You will always be better than me at

_____ .

41

If you were a color, you'd be

_____ .

42

Somehow, I never get bored of your

_____ .

I can't wait to see what happens when

_____ .

I love how you care about

_____ .

I love how you don't care about

_____ .

46

When we're old, let's

_____ .

47

I always want to hear
what you're going to say about

_____ .

48

If you were a junk food item, you'd be

_____ .

49

It's absolutely the best when you

_____ .

50

I am so

_____

that

_____ .

You're the best!

Created, published, and distributed by Knock Knock
11111 Jefferson Blvd. #5167
Culver City, CA 90231
knockknockstuff.com
Knock Knock is a registered trademark of Knock Knock LLC
Fill in the Love is a registered trademark of Knock Knock LLC

MIX
Paper from
responsible sources
FSC® C017606

UPC: 825703-50072-1   ISBN: 978-160106690-9

#fillinthelove